MW00902492

Hi! My name is Quincy Kadin and I am a high school student in Los Angeles. This is my first book! Pretty exciting right?

Throughout my life, I have had an ongoing battle with mental illness. More specifically, anxiety. This impacted me for as long as I remember. Whether it was in school, friendships, or even at my house, I felt as if I couldn't push the feeling away.

When I was twelve years old, I finally was given the opportunity to go to therapy; an opportunity that has changed my life forever. I was able to push past this mental illness, and start to do the things that I had always wanted to do. But at my worst, I always felt alone.

No one in my classes seemed to have been going through the same thing. As I've grown older, I realized that that was not true. Many kids go through this. I wrote this book to not only help kids through their anxious moments, but help them realize that everyone has a little bit of this feeling inside them.

Frankie's Fishy Feelings

Story by Quincy Kadin

Illustrations by Adhemas Batista

Frankie is a 5-year-old
Tigershark.

She loves to swim, go on
playdates, and explore!

One sunny day, Frankie was swimming
with her friend Max.

When she suddenly realized that
kindersharken was starting the next day!

That night, while getting her
kindersharken supplies ready, a feeling
started brewing in her belly.

It grumbled.
It did somersaults.

It felt a little bit like she was
going to throw up.

She tried to ignore it while her
mom tucked her into bed.

But as nighttime went on, the feeling got bigger. And bigger. And bigger.

Until all Frankie could think about
was this icky, yucky, sick feeling.
Finally, she fell asleep.

She woke up in the morning, grabbed her bag, and stepped on the bus. But the feeling was still there.

And the feeling grew. And Frankie couldn't stop it. And it grew until this icky, yucky, sick feeling took over her body.

When they pulled up to school, Frankie started to cry. And shake. And she felt like she couldn't move. The feeling covered every inch of her.

But she shoved it deep down inside her shark body. She walked inside to school and into her kindersharken class.

She made a new friend named Shelly
and met her teacher Mrs. Kelp.

But that night, laying in bed, the icky, yucky, sick feeling came back. And again, it grew and grew and grew. And again, the feeling covered her.

Frankie felt like she couldn't do anything without this feeling telling her not to.

Popping into her stomach when she
would like to go to school or see a friend.
So she told her mom about the feeling.
And her mom took her to a therapist.

Frankie told the therapist what was happening. And began to learn how to manage the icky, yucky, sick feeling.

The next morning, when it came back,
she blew 1, 2, 3, 4, 5 big bubbles.

And the feeling got smaller. It didn't go away completely, but she was able to go to school. She even rode the trikes with Shelly!

The next week at therapy, she learned to feel her feet in her flippers. Working from her heels to her toes.

Again, the icky, yucky, sick feeling
went away.

So she went roller-skating.

The next day as she walked into her music class, she started to feel her belly brewing. So, like her therapist showed her, she counted her fingers.

Thumb, index, middle, ring, little. Little, ring, middle, index thumb. And slowly, it faded away.

Frankie had learned something important. This icky, yucky, sick feeling was called anxiety. And anxiety is actually very normal, she just needed ways to manage it.

Now, Frankie is in control!
Not this feeling.

TOOLBOX

Frankie's Anxiety Toolbox:

- Pick the color of your favorite sea creature.
  Notice everything around you that is that color.

- Name all the sea creatures that you can think of.

- Doodle ocean animals on paper!

- Imagine you are blowing BIG bubbles and blow 5 in a row.

- Feel your feet in your shoes, work from your heels to your toes.

Acknowledgments:

First off, I want to thank my first therapist Lindsey Bergman, Founding Director of the UCLA Pediatric OCD Intensive Outpatient Program and the Associate Director of the UCLA Child and Adolescent OCD and Anxiety Program, for giving me the tools that I still use in my everyday life.

Not only has she helped me, but she has helped countless others by providing these strategies for children. Next, I want to thank my family for helping me complete this project. Finally, I want to thank Adhemas Batista, my partner, for bringing my story to life. His illustrations help portray the emotions that we all face.

Printed in the USA
CPSIA information can be obtained
at www.ICGtesting.com
LVHW061535290124
770078LV00004B/65